Foreword

Two years after the 1969 Stonewall riots,
protested vociferously at the annual mee
Psychiatric Association (APA), claiming tl
of homosexuality as a mental disorder stigmatized ana promoteu
discrimination against them.

The APA subsequently dropped this designation in order to reduce
the stigma, and not because of science. Indeed, many practising
psychiatrists continued to protest that political pressures were not a good
reason to change. Few, however, would have anticipated that the victims
would become the persecutors. The outrageously unethical notion
of banning psychotherapy for people who go voluntarily to a trained
professional seeking to lessen their same-sex desires, even in order to
marry or protect existing families, could not have been imagined.

But that is what therapists in the UK now face. The general public are
unaware that activists have achieved such extreme restrictions without
scientific justification. Mr O'Callaghan and Dr May have performed
a service in analyzing some of the distortions used by the activists to
"justify" their unethical behaviours. They have mostly focused on the
writings of the leading homosexual academic psychiatrist in Britain,
Professor Michael King.

I debated with Professor King and Mr Peter Tatchell recently in London,
and was astonished to hear their weak arguments. Let it be understood
very clearly:

1. There is a <u>very large</u> body of quality scientific literature
   demonstrating successful treatment of people unhappy with same-
   sex desires who became comfortably heterosexual. I referred to
   about 50 such publications.

2. There is <u>no</u> significant body of scientific literature demonstrating
   harm from such therapy, only some personal anecdotes.

3. "Sexual orientation" is a way of thinking about people's sexual
   preferences. There is no specific location in the brain for "sexual
   orientation" and no scientific justification to claim that a person
   with same-sex attraction cannot with psychotherapy discover – or
   re-discover – opposite-sex attraction. If people who once identified

themselves as heterosexual can in later life identify as homosexual, then the opposite must also hold.

5. Despite thirty years of research and many well-publicised claims, there is no substantiated body of evidence that homosexuality is inherited genetically. Neither is there any scientific support for an anatomical (in the brain), biochemical, physiological, physical or organic cause. There is no scientific support for a recent speculative fantasy that homosexuality might be caused by uterine hormones on the foetus.

8 There is no physical or biological laboratory test to determine who is, and who isn't, homosexual. It is purely a self-identification.

As one who grew up in England, I am embarrassed at the attitudes of organizations like the UK Council for Psychotherapy (UKCP). I am deeply offended that my profession has become besmirched with the outrageous bigotry demonstrated in the "Guidelines" relating to people troubled by same-sex desires. These are blatantly biased and have no scientific support.

The notion that a history of oppression justifies a gross interference with a process of treatment whose success has been demonstrated is absurd. Every ethical therapist offers psychotherapeutic help only to those who voluntarily seek it. In no other area of medicine or psychiatry would comparable client requests be denied. The UKCP ought to be ashamed of its unethical stance.

Dr May has added a fine critique of some of the very questionable claims that were submitted on behalf of a very small group, the LGB Special Interest Group of the Royal College of Psychiatrists.

Advocates for same-sex marriage and parenting claim that such homes show no differences in the functional development of children. In fact research does not support such claims.

Dr Joseph Berger
MBBS (Hons) FRCP(C) DABPN

Consulting Psychiatrist, Toronto
Distinguished Life Fellow, American Psychiatric Association

Dermot O'Callaghan
Peter May

BEYOND CRITIQUE
The Misuse of Science by UK Professional Mental Health Bodies

2nd (expanded) Edition: When Ideology Replaces Science

Core Issues Trust

Dermot O'Callaghan, MA (Cantab) Studied Mechanical Sciences at Cambridge University and, after five years in industry, spent his working career as a management consultant in a variety of sectors, including mental health. In his retirement he has taken an interest in the way that science in recent decades has sought to understand the causes and consequences of same-sex attraction. He has followed with interest the ways in which science has been used (and sometimes misused) in society's debates and in the shaping of social policy, including the increasingly robust actions of mental health professional bodies to prevent even a married man from being helped to reduce his unwanted same-sex attractions in order to save his marriage.

Dermot is married, with one son and two grandchildren. He is a member of the General Synod of the Church of Ireland. He is a Council of Reference member of Core Issues Trust.

Peter G. May, MRCGP studied Medicine at the Royal Free Hospital School of Medicine in London. He subsequently trained in General Practice in Southampton, before becoming a Partner at the Grove Medical Practice in Shirley, Southampton. He has had a particular interest in exposing the claims of fraudulent healers, whether New Age Therapists or religious 'miracle' workers. His study, "Claimed Contemporary Miracles" was published in the Medico-Legal Journal in 2003. Now retired, he concentrates on various writing projects.

Peter is married, with four married children and thirteen grandchildren. He was a member of the General Synod of the Church of England from 1985-2010.

Beyond Critique (Revised Edition) - Preface

We usually take it for granted that the historic institutions of the western world are bastions of certainty. If they make an authoritative statement the mass media assume that anyone who disagrees is somewhere on a spectrum between a villain and a fool. This is particularly the case where scientific matters are concerned.

It may come as a shock to find that such trust is not always securely grounded. In particular, a politically correct ideology is rapidly encroaching on the western world, an ideology which is subtly reshaping the values of society as regards attitudes to sexuality. The shock lies not in the fact of reshaping, for society must always adapt or die, but in the discovery that significant areas of scientific endeavour are now influenced by ideology rather than by pure research.

The book *Destructive Trends in Mental Health: The well intentioned path to harm* (eds Nicholas Cummings and Rogers Wright[1]) well expresses these concerns in an American context:

> ... gay groups within the American Psychological Association have repeatedly tried to persuade the association to adopt ethical standards that prohibit therapists from offering psychotherapeutic services designed to ameliorate "gayness," on the basis that such efforts are unsuccessful and harmful to the consumer. Psychologists who do not agree with this premise are termed homophobic. Such efforts are especially troubling because they abrogate the patient's right to choose the therapist and determine therapeutic goals. They also deny the reality of data demonstrating that psychotherapy can be effective in changing sexual preferences in patients who have a desire to do so. (Preface p xxx (sic))

On p 17 (by Cummings and O'Donohue) there is a section entitled, *Is Treating Homosexuality Unethical?* It says,

> Although the APA is reluctant or unable to evaluate questionable practices and has thus avoided addressing the issue of best practices, this did not prevent its Council of Representatives in 2002 from stampeding into a motion to declare the treatment of homosexuality unethical. This was done with the intent of

---

1 Routledge (2005) Cummings is a past president of the American Psychological Association; Wright is a past president of two of the Association's divisions.

perpetuating homosexuality, even when the homosexual patient willingly and even eagerly seeks treatment. The argument was that because homosexuality is not an illness, its treatment is unnecessary and unethical. Curiously, and rightly so, there was no counterargument against psychological interventions conducted by gay therapists to help patients be gay, such as those over many decades by leading psychologist and personal friend Donald Clark (the author of the best-selling *Living Gay*) and many others. Vigorously pushed by the gay lobby, it was eventually seen by a sufficient number of Council members as runaway political correctness and was defeated by the narrowest of margins. In a series of courageous letters to the various components of APA, former president Robert Perloff referred to the willingness of many psychologists to trample patients' rights to treatment in the interest of political correctness. He pointed out that making such treatment unethical would deprive a patient of a treatment of choice because the threat of sanctions would eliminate any psychologist who engaged in such treatment. Although the resolution was narrowly defeated, this has not stopped its proponents from deriding colleagues who provide such treatment to patients seeking it. (p 17,18)

Perloff commends the book saying, "Wright and Cummings persuasively and forcefully dramatize how the mental health professions will enhance patient benefits by removing from the therapeutic process such destructive barriers as political correctness and intrusive ideologies." Yet another past president of the APA, Jack G Wiggins, says that the authors "provide cogent examples of how in mental health circles today misguided idealism and social sophistry guarantee that good science and practice will not go unpunished."

This withering salvo of criticism from some of the most respected people in the field should be enough to make even the most trusting person aware that all is not well in the world of psychology – at least in the USA. Yet in America it is still permissible for therapists to assist clients to endeavour to reduce same-sex attractions if they so desire (although in California in 2012 such therapy has been banned for children under the age of consent).

But such controversial measures could not happen in the UK, could they? Events in the UK have actually overtaken the American practice, however. In a letter to *The Independent* on 5th February 2010, Professor Andrew Samuels, then Chair of the UK Council for Psychotherapy, wrote:

No responsible psychotherapist will attempt to "convert" a client from homosexuality to heterosexuality. It is clinically and ethically misguided. Any member of the United Kingdom Council for Psychotherapy who tried to do so would have to face the music.

A consequence of this is that therapists in the UK are now being forbidden to assist a client to reduce same-sex attractions, primarily on the grounds that such attempts are dangerous. Therapists who disagree are being threatened and disciplined.

The reader would rightly be wary of any therapist who promised an easy conversion from one end of the homosexual/ heterosexual scale to the other. On the other hand the thought of a man being given a blanket refusal to receive help to reduce his unwanted same-sex attractions even in order to hold his family together raises some important issues of human rights and freedoms which we ignore at our peril.

Closely related to these things is the question of same-sex marriage, which is currently the subject of much debate. Many people uncritically assume that this is merely a matter of extending the beneficial institution of marriage to people who are unjustly excluded at present, and that there would be no negative consequences for public health. We question this position.

The following pages will examine three documents: *Page*

highlighting some of their content and assessing the degree to which they are answerable to objective scientific research.

The first two of these were discussed by Dermot O'Callaghan in the previous edition of this booklet. This revised version adds Peter May's analysis of the third document.

Beyond Critique - 1
The Royal College of Psychiatrists

RC
PSYCH
ROYAL COLLEGE OF
PSYCHIATRISTS

Submission of the Royal College of Psychiatrists LGB Special Interest Group to the Church of England 'Listening Exercise' (2007)

by Dermot O'Callaghan

The lesbian and gay special interest group of the Royal College of Psychiatrists made a submission to the "Church of England Listening Exercise", dated 31st October 2007 and signed by Professor Michael King. It is to be welcomed as being a concise document which grounds its arguments in the scientific literature in a way that appears to be without parallel in the UK. In short, it is 'best of breed'.

1. Two different versions of the text

The submission (hereinafter referred to as *Version 1*)[2] cites no fewer than nineteen scientific papers to support its arguments. These are referenced in the present discussion as (ref 1) to (ref 19). Thus, in the opening section the Royal College gives an outline of the history of LGB people in Europe over the past two centuries and references a paper by King & Bartlett 1999 (ref 1).

A link at the end of the submission (which may have been added retrospectively) links to another version of the submission (hereinafter *Version 2*)[3] which omits Professor King's name and the date and adds some striking graphics (various pictures of human hands). In this version the references to the various scientific papers are embedded in the text of the submission (though ref 19 is omitted). *This version appears to carry the imprimatur of the Royal College of Psychiatrists* as opposed to just the special interest group. [Both the above were accessed on 21 December 2012.]

Version 2 appears to be verbally almost identical to Version 1, but it has one significant difference under heading 2 (*The origins of homosexuality*). Version 1 says, "It would appear that sexual orientation is biological in nature, determined by a complex interplay of genetic

2   www.rcpsych.ac.uk/pdf/Submission%20to%20the%20Church%20of%20England.pdf
3   www.rcpsych.ac.uk/workinpsychiatry/specialinterestgroups/gaylesbian/submissiontothecofe.aspx

factors _and_ the early uterine environment" (emphasis added). In version 2, however, the word '_and_' is changed to '_and/ or_'. In simple language, the change is from 'genes and hormones' to 'genes and/ or hormones.'

Royal College Original Submission to Church of England (2007)	Revised version
"Genes _and_ hormones"	"Genes _and/or_ hormones"

The significance of this change is considered below.

2. Causation of Homosexuality

2.1 'Genes and/ or hormones' is a self-defeating formula

Subject to clarification from the Royal College, it would appear that the 'and/ or' version is the preferred text; it is found in the more sophisticated version of the document (the version with graphics). The _and/ or_ formula allows the possibilities that causation may be:
- entirely genetic
- or entirely hormonal ('the early uterine environment')
- or a combination of both genes and hormones.

But there is a relentless logic inherent in this formula. If the Royal College believes that the causes may turn out to be 'entirely genetic', then it follows that any evidence of _hormonal_ causation that we believe we have today is merely illusory. And if the causation turns out to be 'entirely hormonal', then any evidence of _genetic_ causation that we believe we have today is illusory. This means that the Royal College is prepared to accept that all supposed evidence that we have today for either genetic or hormonal causation may be illusory – in other words, it is at best very weak. But if indeed there is no compelling evidence for either genes or hormones, the College's statement, "It would appear that sexual orientation is biological in nature", is not based on any sound scientific evidence.

2.2 Unwarranted rejection of early childhood experiences as a causal factor

The Royal College says,"Despite almost a century of psychoanalytic and psychological speculation, there is no substantive evidence to support the suggestion that the nature of parenting or early childhood experiences play any role in the formation of a person's fundamental heterosexual or homosexual orientation". Yet only the previous year (2006) a major national cohort study in Denmark by Frisch *et al* (with a sample size of two million people) said: "Our study provides population-based, prospective evidence that childhood family experiences are important determinants of heterosexual and homosexual marriage decisions in adulthood."[4] Also a highly regarded 1994 study by EO Laumann et al[5] based on the US National Health and Social Life Study, said (p307) that a pattern of homosexuality similar to those of biologically-based traits such as left-handedness or intelligence is "exactly what we do not find." Further, in discussing male homosexuality, it said (p309) that the theory that "the environment in which people grow up affects their sexuality in very basic ways" is "exactly one way to read many of the patterns that we have found."

2.3 Erroneous reference to Bell & Weinberg 1978

The Royal College supports its argument by a reference to *Bell & Weinberg 1978* (ref 2). But that study does not address the question of homosexual origins. This reference therefore appears to be simply mistaken.[6]

2.4 Citation of a study by Mustanski which found nothing

The Royal College cites a study by Mustanski *et al* 2005 (ref 3) implying that it supports a genetic causation. But that study, which undertook a search for genetic linkages to homosexuality, found no linkage of statistical significance. A subsequent study by Rice failed to confirm even the 'possible' linkages suggested by Mustanski. One presumes that the Royal College have chosen their most persuasive study to support their argument in favour of genetic causation, yet Mustanski provides no evidence at all for this view.

---

4   M Frisch et al (2006). Childhood Family Correlates of Heterosexual and Homosexual Marriages: A National
      Cohort Study of Two Million Danes. Archives of Sexual Behavior 35, 533-47

5   The Social Organization of Sexuality, E O Laumann et al, University of Chicago Press 1994

6   It seems likely that the intended reference is to Bell, Weinberg & Hammersmith (1981). But even after making this presumed correction there is a problem. An authoritative critic has written, "There is a persistently repeated statement in the literature that there is no social connection with the development of same-sex attraction, but the only authority cited is Bell, Weinberg and Hammersmith (1981). There appears to be no subsequent critical statistical evaluation of this work and the attached paper shows that from internal data, there is substantial correlation with social factors." The 'attached paper' is found at http://www. mygenes.co.nz/Bell_WeinbergJHS.pdf It shows that there is an urgent need to revisit Bell, Weinberg and Hammersmith (1981) to re-evaluate the implications of the data collected in that study

2.5 Blanchard (2006) study – bordering on science fiction?

The Royal College also references a paper by Blanchard *et al* 2006 (ref 4) which investigates a possible correlation of male homosexuality with both genes and maternal hormones. This paper discusses some curious patterns in data pooled from five other studies which appear to suggest that:
- if a boy child is born left-handed (a genetically related trait) he has an elevated expectation of identifying as gay in adult life;
- similarly, if a boy is born to a mother who has already given birth to a boy child, the odds of his becoming gay-identified also appear to be elevated (this is considered to be caused by the mother's hormones);
- yet a boy who is born both left-handed and having an older brother does not have a 'doubly enhanced' likelihood of being gay-identified – indeed *his likelihood of being gay is not elevated at all above the average man in society.*

The study wrestles with this strange paradox. The researchers suggest two possible answers:

- either the two factors somehow cancel each other out (though it stretches the imagination to imagine why a genetic factor and a hormonal factor which each tend to produce the same result should cancel each other out);
- or "the combination of the older brother factor with the non-right-handedness factor is toxic enough to lower the probability that the affected fetus will survive." This extraordinary suggestion is that an unborn boy child's left-handedness might interact with the fact that his mother has already had a boy child, to produce a "toxic" effect that is so severe that it may kill the child before birth.

Given the sad history of flawed studies based on distorted samples, it may be pertinent to suggest that the many complexities involved in pooling data from five different studies may have introduced inaccuracies that have led to conclusions that are of questionable value.

Whichever explanation they prefer, the Royal College are advancing a problematic and unconvincing study to support their assertion that homosexuality appears to be 'biological in nature'.

2.6 Why no discussion of twin studies?

But is there really no substantive evidence, as the Royal College says, to support the suggestion that childhood experiences play any role in the formation of one's sexual orientation?

In addition to the studies by Frisch and Laumann mentioned above, studies of twins provide an important tool for separating biological from environmental factors; indeed they have been at the centre of the debate for more than twenty years. Very surprisingly the Royal College makes no reference at all to twin studies– yet no scientific discussion of the causation of homosexuality can be considered satisfactory without consideration of the evidence they provide.

An important study by Bailey *et al* (2000), found that if one identical male twin identified as gay, the second twin usually didn't (in only one in nine cases, or 11.1%, was there concordance for homosexuality). Thus 89% of causation does not appear to be explained by biological factors (and so analogies such as race are seriously misleading). Similar figures have been found in other large studies. This strongly suggests the importance of environmental factors such as early life experiences in the formation of sexual orientation.

2.7 Causation of homosexuality – concluding summary

The Royal College appears to have incorrectly cited a study by Bell & Weinberg (1978) as having failed to find evidence of early childhood experiences (environmental effects) having any role in the formation of a person's sexuality.

It advances only two studies in support of its contention for biological causes. One of these, (Mustanski) did not find any genetic cause; and the other (Blanchard) does not provide any serious support for the Royal College's argument. These two studies provide no foundation at all for arguing a case for biological causation.

By contrast, Laumann, Frisch and various twin studies are quite clear: they show that it is simply not plausible that biology is the sole causal agent.

3. Causation of elevated levels of mental illness among LGB people

It is widely recognised that same-sex attracted people experience higher mental illness – including depression and suicide attempts – than the general population. An important question is whether this is mainly caused by society or is related to homosexuality itself. If it is caused by negative attitudes in society ('homophobia') then its diminution requires a cultural shift. If, on the other hand, it is related to something inherent in homosexuality itself or related to such things as gay culture or lifestyles, then cultural change in society will not resolve the problem. The Royal College submission is quite clear in its attribution of responsibility:

> "the experiences of discrimination in society and possible rejection by friends, families and others, such as employers, means that some LGB people experience a greater than expected prevalence of mental health and substance misuse problems".

In other words, they say that the problem lies with discrimination in society, not within the condition itself or the chosen lifestyles of some LGB people.

Three scientific papers are referenced – *but all of them decline to attribute causation to societal attitudes*, contrary to the Royal College's position.

Gilman *et al* 2001 (ref 6) says,

"the precise causal mechanism at this point remains unknown. Therefore, studies are needed that directly test meditational hypotheses to evaluate, for example, the relative salience of social stigmatization and lifestyle factors as potential contributors to psychiatric morbidity among gays and lesbians."

Royal College (2007) Position	Scientific Paper 1: Gilman et al 2001 (Ref 6)
Discrimination in society ... **means** that some LGB people experience greater than expected mental health and substance abuse problems_	the **precise causal mechanism at this point remains unknown**. Therefore, studies are needed that directly test mediational hypotheses to evaluate, for example, the relative salience of social stigmatization and of psychosocial and lifestyle factors as potential contributors

Bailey 1999 (ref 7) says,

> ".... many people will conclude that widespread prejudice

against homosexual people causes them to be unhappy or worse, mentally ill. Commitment to [this position] would be premature, however, and should be discouraged. In fact, a number of potential interpretations need to be considered, and progress toward scientific understanding will be achieved only by eliminating competing explanations ..."

In other words Bailey cautions against the very position that the Royal College chooses to adopt.

Royal College (2007) Position	Scientific Paper 2: Bailey et al 1999 (Ref 7)
Discrimination in society ... *means* that some LGB people experience greater than expected mental health and substance abuse problems_	"... many people will conclude that widespread *prejudice* against homosexual people causes them to be unhappy or worse, mentally ill. ***Commitment to [this position]*** would be premature, however, and ***should be discouraged*** . In fact, a number of potential interpretations need to be considered ...

The lead author of the third paper (ref 5) is none other than Professor Michael King himself, the signatory of the Royal College's submission to the Church of England. His paper says,

"There are several explanations for our findings. It may be that prejudice in society against gay men and lesbians leads to greater psychological distress ... Conversely, gay men and lesbians may have lifestyles that make them vulnerable to psychological disorder."

Royal College (2007) Position	Scientific Paper 3: King et al 2003 (Ref 5)
Discrimination in society ... *means* that some LGB people experience greater than expected mental health and substance abuse problems_	It **may be** that **prejudice in society** against gay men and lesbians leads to greater psychological distress ... **Conversely**, gay men and lesbians **may have lifestyles** that make them vulnerable to psychological disorder._

So all three of the referenced papers say the same thing: the evidence does not enable the researchers to determine whether the problem lies externally in society or internally with co-morbidities or lifestyle factors. It is clearly important not to jump to conclusions.

This raises the question of why the Royal College places the blame squarely on society, distorting the judgement of the scientific research – even the research of Professor King himself. The contrast between his careful statement to the scientific community and his submission to the Church of England is significant:

It is clear that when addressing the scientific community Professor King leaves open the matter of causation – as do all the other scientific papers. His message to the Church of England, however, places the blame squarely on discrimination.

It is also ironically true that the Bell & Weinberg (1978) study, which seems to have been mistakenly referenced by the Royal College above, identifies *relationship breakup* as a major factor in suicide (and since gay people have more relationships and thus more breakups they are for that reason more vulnerable to depression and suicide).

The Royal College should revise its submission to the Church of England to acknowledge that the scientific research does not attribute to societal attitudes the problem of elevated stress among LGB people, but rather insists that the question of causation has not been resolved.

4. Causation of short duration of sexual relationships

Citing the work of Mays & Cochran (ref 8) and McWhirter & Mattison (ref 9), the Royal College says that there is "considerable variability in the quality and durability of same-sex, cohabiting relationships" and that a "considerable amount of the instability in gay and lesbian partnerships arises from lack of support within society, the church or the family for such relationships."

Once again, in other words, it's largely society's fault. But in fact the Mays & Cochran study does not refer at all to the quality or durability of same-sex relationships, but rather confirms the consensus of the scientific papers in the foregoing section, to the effect that "it is unclear whether the greater risk for discriminatory experiences, if it does exist, can account for the observed excess of psychiatric morbidity seen among lesbians and gay men". Its own methodology "precludes drawing causal inferences."

Royal College (2007) Position	Scientific Paper 1: Mays et al 2001 (Ref 8)
A considerable amount of the instability in gay and lesbian partnerships arises from lack of support within society, the church or the family for such relationships	"it is **unclear whether** the greater risk for **discriminatory experiences**, if it does exist, **can account for the observed excess of psychiatric morbidity** seen among lesbians and gay men"

The Royal College says that there is already "good evidence that marriage confers health benefits on heterosexual men and women". Indeed this is true, but without reference to any scientific study the College extrapolates this argument to say that "similar benefits could accrue from same-sex civil unions" (legislation for which had been introduced three years previously, in 2004). Similar logic today (2013) would argue that *same-sex marriage* would deliver these benefits (which civil partnerships failed to deliver).

Yet the Royal College fails to acknowledge a crucial finding of McWhirter and Mattison, that a 'common problem' for male couples is "between their value systems ... for example, holding different values about sexual exclusivity and emotional fidelity can be very problematic and induce jealousy." This issue is discussed at greater length in McWhirter and Mattison's major work The Male Couple (1984) on which their paper (ref 9) is based – that gay men seek 'fidelity' (that is, they want to live together as a couple) yet without 'sexual exclusivity'. This can be achieved only by changing the meaning of the word fidelity. McWhirter and Mattison found that "all couples with a relationship lasting more than five years have incorporated some provision for outside sexual activity in their relationships." They comment that "To arrive at the acceptance of being gay and of extrarelational sex, each of these men has had to alter his own value systems" (The Male Couple, p.252 - 3).

Royal College (2007) Position	Scientific Paper 2: McWhirter & Mattison 1996 (Ref 9)
A considerable amount of the instability in gay and lesbian partnerships arises from *lack of support within society, the church or the family* for such relationships	One of the more common problems ... is differences between their value systems. Religious differences and a tendency to make **heterosexual assumptions** about their relationship are often responsible. For example, holding **different values about sexual exclusivity** and emotional fidelity can be very problematic and induce jealousy.

It seems highly probable that rather than civil partnerships (or now 'gay marriage') bringing stability to gay relationships, the tensions inherent in such relationships will lead to rejection of the 'heterosexual assumption' of the requirement of sexual exclusivity in the relationship as noted by McWhirter and Mattison. But we are constantly told that there can only be one type of marriage, so those heterosexual assumptions will *de facto* be removed from marriage itself. If it is acceptable for gay married couples to have outside sexual liaisons, why not for heterosexuals? Rather than help the stability of the relationships of those few gay and lesbian people who will choose to marry, it seems probable that marriage for the heterosexual community will be undermined by a new 'equality' in which marriage is redefined according to the value systems of gay culture noted by McWhirter and Mattison. Children will be taught in school that the value system of 'gay marriage' does not require monogamy. The principle of equality will then demand the same for heterosexual marriage – and children will draw that conclusion automatically anyway. Whatever small benefit may accrue to the very few LGB people who will marry, is likely to be overwhelmed by the negative impact on heterosexual marriage, which has until now been the chosen relationship for the majority of the population. And what about the bisexuals, who will want three in a marriage?

Citing *Kiecolt-Glaser & Newton* 2001 (ref 10) and *Johnson et al* 2000 (ref 11), the Royal College argues that since there is good evidence that marriage confers benefits on husband and wife, similar benefits could accrue to same- sex couples in civil partnerships. But Kiecolt-Glaser and Newton argue that there are *differential costs and benefits in a marriage*, which are *gender-specific.* The costs and benefits that accrue to the wife are different from those that accrue to the husband. It does not therefore follow that if the gender of the spouse changes (eg a man marries a man rather than a woman) that the usual benefits of marriage are to be expected. Indeed any assumption of such read-across is nothing more than speculation. The Johnson et al study did not include any same-sex partners at all.

Royal College (2007) Position	Scientific Paper 3: Kiecolt-Glaser 2001 (Ref 10) Scientific Paper 4: Johnson et al (ref 11)
"There is already good evidence that marriage confers health benefits on heterosexual men and women and similar *benefits could accrue from same-sex civil unions.* "	"Contemporary models of gender ... furnish alternative perspectives on the differential costs and benefits of marriage for men's and women's health." [ie The *benefits of marriage are very gender-specific*] Johnson et al had no same-sex partners in study

The Royal College continues to hope that civil unions will bring benefits. It says, "Legal and social recognition of same-sex relationships is likely to reduce discrimination, increase the stability of same sex relationships and lead to better physical and mental health for gay and lesbian people." But in the cited paper King & Bartlett 2005 (ref 12) Professor King admits that "we do not know" whether the short duration of male relationships is due to intrinsic or extrinsic factors.

Royal College (2007) Position	Scientific Paper 5: King, Bartlett 2006 (Ref 12)
Legal recognition of civil partnerships seems likely to stabilise same-sex relationships	" *We do not know* whether gay male, same sex relationships are less enduring because of *something intrinsic* to being male or a gay male, the gay male *subculture* that encourages multiple partners, or a failure of *social recognition* of their relationships. The *'social experiment'* that civil unions provide will enable us to disentangle the health and social effects of this complex question"

He looks to the 'social experiment' of civil unions to provide some answers. For many people, of course, this is a social experiment too far and the risks inherent in what Professor King describes as 'this complex question' are too great and have not been thought through.

After all the discussion of possible reasons for the short duration of same-sex relationships, a fair summary of the science would seem to be 'we don't know'.

5. Psychotherapy and Reparative Therapy for LGB People

The Royal College urges therapists to take care in the initial diagnosis of clients who present with issues that they may think are caused by homosexual attractions, referencing *King et al* 2007. Therapists may wrongly regard homosexuality as the root cause of any depression, anxiety etc. This is good advice and should be followed by all therapists.

Royal College (2007) Position	Scientific Answer: King et al 2007 (Ref 13)
LGB people "may be misunderstood by therapists who regard their homosexuality as the root cause of any presenting problem such as depression or anxiety"	"Both therapist and client need to be aware of the dominant discourses and stereotypes in the LGBT world, because, if they fail to do so, the possibility of collusion and shared assumptions may limit the depth and utility of the therapy." "... no randomised trials of effectiveness of ... (gay affirmative) treatments".

The paper also discusses its assessment of *gay-affirmative* therapy saying, "We identified no randomised trials of effectiveness of general or specialised mental health treatments for LGBT people. Nor did we identify any 'before and after' or cohort studies assessing outcomes of therapy and counselling for LGBT people. There was no consistency in the instruments used to assess past or current therapy, satisfaction with care or other outcomes. None of the studies reviewed measured mental health outcomes using validated psychometric measures."

The Royal College next addresses the important question of whether change in sexual orientation is ever possible, and whether it is dangerous to attempt such change. Citing Bartlett et al 2001 (ref 14) it says, "A small minority of therapists will even go so far as to attempt to change their client's sexual orientation. This can be deeply damaging. Although there is now a number of therapists and organisations in the USA and in the UK that claim that therapy can help homosexuals to become heterosexual, there is no evidence that such change is possible. The best evidence for efficacy of any treatment comes from randomised clinical trials and no such trial has been carried out in this field." It is important to acknowledge, however, that as noted in the previous paragraph, the very same considerations apply to gay-affirmative therapy.

The twin claims that there is no evidence that change is possible and that attempts to change are deeply damaging need to be considered most carefully. Insofar as the issue is framed in polarised terms (that 'change' means complete change from homosexual to heterosexual), the large amount of evidence that fluidity of orientation (moving up or down the homosexual/ heterosexual continuum) is a common phenomenon, not least among women, is neglected. For example, a respected 10-year longitudinal study of non-heterosexual women by Diamond[7] found that "all women reported declines in their ratio of same-sex to opposite-sex behaviour over time."

Royal College (2007) Version	Bartlett, King & Phillips 2001 (Ref 14)
"A small minority of therapists will even go so far as to attempt to change their client's sexual orientation. This can be *deeply damaging* ... there is **no evidence that such change is possible** ... no randomised clinical trial has been carried out."	This does reflect what the paper says. But the study used -*no measures of harm,* and - *no measures of change*. It merely reflects the *opinions* of certain therapists.
BUT: Jones & Yarhouse in 2007 published the results of the best study to date. Their findings "contradict the commonly expressed view ... that change of sexual orientation is impossible and that the attempt to change is highly likely to produce harm ...". *[Jones & Yarhouse used a validated measure of psychological distress to assess harm, but found benefit rather than harm.] Their study was updated in 2011 with similar results.*	

A paper by Jones and Yarhouse[8], the best study to date, seems to have been published a few months before the Royal College's submission but is not discussed. The study improved on earlier ones in that it followed a cohort of people *prospectively* through therapeutic programmes (not knowing what the outcome would be) and used well-tried psychological

7   Developmental Psychology Copyright 2008 by the American Psychological Association 2008, Vol. 44, No. 1, 5–14
8   http://www.tandfonline.com/doi/full/10.1080/0092623X.2011.607052

measures of sexual orientation and psychological distress (to identify indications of harm). They said that their findings "contradict the commonly expressed view ... that change of sexual orientation is impossible and that the attempt to change is highly likely to produce harm ..."

We turn now to the papers discussed by the Royal College. The submission refers to two well-known studies. The first is by Dr Robert Spitzer, who was the leading scientist in the de-listing of homosexuality from the Diagnostic Manual of Mental Disorders in the USA in 1973. He subsequently encountered a number of people who claimed to have moved away from homosexuality, and he decided to undertake a study of this phenomenon. The Royal College describes the results of the study thus:

> "The first study claimed that change was possible for a small minority (13%) of LGB people, most of who (sic) could be regarded as bisexual at the outset of therapy".

In fact, the actual claims of Spitzer's study could hardly be more different:

> "The majority of participants gave reports of change from a predominantly or exclusively homosexual orientation before therapy to a predominantly or exclusively heterosexual orientation in the past year".

Spitzer's finding of change for *'the majority'* is transformed by the Royal College into *'a small minority'*. And his claim that most of his participants had been *'predominantly or exclusively'* homosexual at the outset is trivialised to say that they were *mostly bisexual* rather than homosexual.

Royal College (2007) Version	Spitzer (Ref 15)
The study "claimed that change was possible for - a **small minority (13%)** of LGB people, - **most of whom were bisexual** at outset."	The study actually said, - **majority** of participants gave reports of change - from a **predominantly or exclusively homosexual** orientation before therapy

It is most disturbing that the Royal College of Psychiatrists should so misrepresent the findings of a respected scientist.

Such radical misrepresentation of the work of a fellow-scientist is beyond words. It inevitably casts a shadow over the Royal College of Psychiatrists as a venerable and trusted institution. It gives clear evidence that in the field of sexual ethics the Royal College is being driven by a special interest group whose fundamental motivation is not scientific discovery but ideological dogma.[9]

The second study referenced is *Shidlo and Schroeder* 2002, which is described as finding "little effect as well as considerable harm." There are several aspects of this study that must be taken into account:

HELP US DOCUMENT THE DAMAGE OF HOMOPHOBIC THERAPIES

In association with the National Lesbian and Gay Health Association, we are conducting research on the outcome of treatments that claim to "cure" homosexuality. Our purpose is to document the damage that we believe occurs when a lesbian, gay or bisexual client receives psychological help from a provider who promises to change a person's sexual orientation.

- It set out to recruit participants who were <u>dissatisfied</u> with their experience of therapy (see in sidebar copy of initial advertisement, which was later changed) just as the Spitzer study set out to find participants who were <u>satisfied</u> with their therapy

- It found that a majority (61%) of people found <u>some help</u> from the therapy

- A bigger majority (85%) found <u>some harm</u>

We are looking for individuals who have experienced such a program and who are willing to talk about it confidentially by telephone, email or by filling out a written survey.

For more information, please contact Dr. Michael Schroeder and Dr. Ariel Shidlo telephone (212) 353-2558, email gayconvert@aol.com

But since no <u>measure</u> of harm was used, and since such a retrospective study cannot in any case establish causation, it is quite wrong for the Royal College to imply that the therapies caused 'considerable harm'.

The reality is that the above-mentioned Jones & Yarhouse study is the best scientific evidence that we have, and it did not find that people were harmed on average. Yet the Royal College refers to the danger of 'harm' and 'damage' in such a way as to imply that attempts to reduce same-sex attraction are in themselves harmful.

The Royal College now puts forward two studies (refs 17 & 18) co-authored by Professor King, which are described as 'oral histories' – respectively the views of professionals and of patients – both dated 2004. Both studies collected historical recollections from the 1960's and

9   Spitzer has been viciously attacked by gay activists for more than a decade because of his study findings. Already in 2005 he referred to 'battle fatigue' in repelling attacks. Wikipedia reports that eventually in 2012 "he spoke with the editor of the Archives of Sexual Behavior about writing a retraction, but the editor declined." Retraction is normally based on gross errors or deception and these do not apply here.

1970's, when draconian treatments using electric shocks and drugs to try to 'cure' homosexuality were widespread. These are not used today, and it is important that the general public should realise that today's 'talking therapies' are totally different.

It is interesting to note in passing that Professor King reported in 2004 that only "a small minority [of professionals] believed that current practice denied people distressed by their homosexuality an effective means to change their sexual orientation." This is the very position that he opposes today in his submission to the Church of England.

Royal College (2007)	Oral History (Professionals' views) King et al 2004 (Ref 17)
Treatments in 1960s and 1970s were very damaging and affected no change in orientation	The practices of this period are *no longer relevant* to the present debate.
"Only a small minority believed that current practice denied people distressed by their homosexuality an effective means to change their sexual orientation". *How different today!*	

The second study documents some reflections of patients of their recollections of experiences of therapy decades ago. Once again, it is of historical interest only, and hardly appropriate.

Royal College (2007)	Oral History (Patients' views) King et al 2004 (Ref 18)
Treatments in 1960s and 1970s were very damaging and affected no change in orientation	As before, the practices of this period are *no longer relevant* to the present debate.
A poignant comment from the study: *"Many participants felt they lacked parental affection during childhood and adolescence"*	

These two historical studies allow the Royal College to say, "we know from historical evidence that treatments to change sexual orientation that were common in the 1960s and 1970s were very damaging to those patients who underwent them and affected no change in their sexual orientation." This information is superfluous to the present situation and

may be misleading to the incautious reader. One poignant comment from the latter study, however, is that, "Many participants felt they lacked parental affection during childhood and adolescence"
The final study, ref 19, is by Dougas Haldeman, a respected gay-affirming scholar.

Royal College (2007)	Haldeman, Gay Rights, Patient Rights 2002 (Ref 19)
People are happiest and are likely to reach their potential when they are able to *integrate* the various aspects of the self as fully as possible	... gay-affirmative therapists need to take seriously the experiences of their religious clients, *refraining from* encouraging an abandonment of their spiritual traditions in favour of a more gay-affirming doctrine or *discouraging their exploration of conversion treatments*.

Haldeman's conclusion:
...we must respect the choices of all who seek to live life in accordance with their own identities; and *if there are those who seek* to resolve the conflict between sexual orientation and spirituality with *conversion therapy*, they must not be discouraged. *It is their choice* ...

He is cited in version 1 of the Royal College's submission, in support of the contention that people "are happiest and are likely to reach their potential when they are able to integrate the various aspects of the self as fully as possible." The implication is that people who feel same-sex attraction will be happiest when they are encouraged to shape their lives around that inclination, regardless of other factors. Haldeman is much more balanced, however. He says that "... gay-affirmative therapists need to take seriously the experiences of their religious clients, refraining from encouraging an abandonment of their spiritual traditions in favour of a more gay-affirming doctrine or discouraging their exploration of conversion treatments."

Haldeman continues, "... we must respect the choices of all who seek to live life in accordance with their own identities; and if there are those who seek to resolve the conflict between sexual orientation and spirituality with conversion therapy, they must not be discouraged. It is their choice ..."

Indeed so. Yet there is no reason why only those clients who are *religious* should have freedom of choice: any man or woman who wishes

to live a heterosexual life should be assisted to do so.
This is not the message that the Royal College of Psychiatrists wishes to give to the Church of England, however. The 'revised version' of the text deletes the reference to Haldeman.

The insistence on client autonomy and choice, which formerly was a cornerstone in psychiatry and psychology, has been set aside. Hopefully the Church of England will demand its reinstatement, in the interests not only of those who are religious, but of all who value the freedom to determine their own life goals.

Beyond Critique - 2
The UK Council for Psychotherapy

by Dermot O'Callaghan

UKCP's Ethical Principles and Codes of Professional Conduct: Guidance on the Practice of Psychological Therapies that Pathologise and/or Seek to Eliminate or Reduce Same Sex Attraction

The UK Council for Psychotherapy has written a document called *Ethical Principles and Code of Professional Conduct* (dated 26th September 2009) which therapists who belong to the Council or its affiliated organisations must uphold at all times.[10] This document sets out in general terms an admirable set of standards for its practitioners.

A subsidiary document, *UKCP's Ethical Principles and Codes of Professional Conduct: Guidance on the Practice of Psychological Therapies that Pathologise and/or Seek to Eliminate or Reduce Same Sex Attraction,* applies the overall principles of the primary document to the specific context of homosexuality

This present critique comments on the second document.
In considering the UKCP Ethical Principles two hypothetical cases will serve as examples

Two hypothetical case studies

- *A young man who would like to marry*

- *A married woman with children*

1. A young man has a lady friend whom he would like to marry. He is concerned, however, that he experiences same-sex attractions which he fears might derail the relationship a few years down the line. For as long as these feelings continue, he is unwilling to take the risk of marrying, not least for the sake of the woman he loves, and would like help in reducing his same-sex attractions.

---

10   http://www.psychotherapy.org.uk/download725.html

2. A woman in her thirties is married with two children. She falls in love with another woman and is torn between leaving her family or staying. She would like help to reduce her same-sex attraction to enable her to keep her family intact.

1. Blanket Ruling: Not in the client's best interests

Each of the above people seeks the advice of an appropriately qualified therapist and is told that science has shown that "agreeing to the client's request for therapy for the reduction of same sex attraction is not in a client's best interests" (2.1 - 1.1(a)).[11] They are both distressed by the news, and by

"Agreeing to the client's request for therapy for the reduction of same sex attraction is not in a client's best interests"

the therapist's advice that they should try to conform their lives to their sexuality.

Such client dilemmas are not uncommon and organisations such as the UKCP have a clear duty of care to avoid harm in their ethical guidance to psychotherapists. A high burden of proof is needed to show that public safety is enhanced by following the UKCP ethical guidance to decline a reasonable client request.

One must question whether research *has* in fact shown that therapy for the reduction of same-sex attraction is always "not in a client's best interests." The ethics document cites Drescher, Shidlo and Schroeder 2002 – the only scientific paper cited in the entire document, and certainly not an adequate basis for refusing all such client requests (where the client has not even been seen, let alone assessed as regards symptoms.

2. Argument 1: Overwhelming evidence of psychological cost

In section 2.1 – 1.1(b) it is stated that "There is overwhelming evidence that undergoing such therapy is at considerable emotional and psychological cost." Where is this "overwhelming evidence" of harm? Dr Stanton Jones in a current commentary on this debate[12] says that

There is "overwhelming evidence that undergoing such therapy is at considerable emotional and psychological cost"

his research (with Dr Mark Yarhouse) into the question of harm "[did] not prove that no one is harmed by the attempt to change, but rather

---

11   Quotations followed by numbered references are taken from the ethical principles document on same sex attraction that is being critiqued here.

12   http://www.wheaton.edu/CACE/Hot-Topics

that the attempt to change does not appear to be harmful on average or inherently harmful. These findings challenge the commonly expressed views of the mental health establishment that change of sexual orientation is impossible or very uncommon, and that the attempt to change is highly likely to produce harm for those who make such an effort." Any argument against the findings of Jones and Yarhouse would need to be based on a study that has followed clients prospectively, administered generally accepted psychological tests to measure distress, and proved that, on average, harm is caused by sexual orientation change efforts. But no such study (other than theirs) has been carried out.

The above words, written in the first edition of this booklet, have proved prophetic. On the Radio 4 Sunday programme, 3rd Feb 2013, Dr Di Hodgson, chair of the Diversity, Equalities and Social Responsibiity Committee of the UKCP said, "whether or not something works doesn't mean that it is ethical or in the public interest or the right thing to do for someone. So we have taken a view in a way which is regardless of the scientific findings." It would be hard to find a clearer declaration of the UKCP's intentional replacement of evidence-based science with ideology-based dogma.

3. Argument 2: A treatment for which there is no illness

Section 1.3 – (e) says that for a psychotherapist to offer treatment that might 'reduce' same sex attraction would be "exploitative" as "to do so would be offering a treatment for which there is no illness." This logic simply falls apart when applied to the two cases outlined above. In neither case is the person described as "ill". But the Guidance implies that if a therapist were to offer treatment to help persons such as these to achieve their life goals, the therapist would thereby be 'exploiting' the client. The error here is to imagine that 'treatments' can be offered only in the case of 'illness'. But one can have 'treatment' for everything from nervousness in public speaking, to weight loss without being declared ill. These people are being denied a human right to treatment intended to help them shape their lives as they wish.

for a psychotherapist to offer treatment that might 'reduce' same sex attraction would be "exploitative" as "to do so would be offering a treatment for which there is no illness."

4. Argument 3: Client autonomy denied because client is 'oppressed'

Section 1.3 – (g) denies client 'autonomy' as sufficient justification for a therapist attempting to reduce same sex attractions, by wrongly suggesting that all such clients are experiencing "externalised and internalised oppression." In our

It is not a sufficient defence for a therapist to argue that ... they were acting in the client's best interests, or ... autonomy, as offering such therapy would be ...reinforcing their externalised and internalised oppression

case examples, it is clearly wrong to imply that the desire to reduce same sex attractions in order to protect one's family is a sign of "oppression" – either external or internal.

5. A Question: Where is the real oppression?

Section 3.1 (ii) concludes that "Based on the above considerations" offering 'Sexual Orientation Change Efforts' is "incompatible with UKCP's Ethical Principles and Code of Professional Conduct." But does it not seem rather that the blanket refusal of such therapies is a form of oppression?

6. Some key questions to be addressed by the UKCP

In order to set out clearly the issues at stake, there are eight questions to which the UKCP needs to provide answers:

1. Is it fair to say that requests for <u>client autonomy</u> such as in the two examples above are entirely reasonable and based on <u>legitimate life goals</u>?

2. What is the <u>evidence</u> that "agreeing to the client's request for therapy for the reduction of same sex attraction is not in a client's best interests" – that is to say, that there are *no cases* <u>in which such a client request should be honoured</u> and that in *no case* would the maxim 'first do no harm' be violated by refusing the client's request.

3. Does the UKCP consider that their reference to Drescher, Shidlo & Schroeder has "shown that offering ... therapy for the reduction of same sex attraction is <u>not in the client's best interests</u>"?

4. Can the UKCP provide specific references to high quality scientific research which shows what they describe as "<u>overwhelming evidence</u> that undergoing such therapy is at considerable emotional and psychological cost." Such evidence would need to be better than that of

Jones & Yarhouse who found to the contrary. That is to say, one or more studies would need to have followed clients <u>prospectively</u>, administered generally accepted psychological <u>tests to measure distress</u>, and proved that, on average, <u>harm is caused</u> by sexual orientation change efforts.

5. In the context of the two cases outlined above, can the UKCP explain how it would be "exploitative" for a therapist to offer treatment that might 'reduce' same sex attraction"?

6. Can the UKCP confirm that there are <u>no circumstances</u> in which it permits therapists to offer treatments <u>"for which there is no illness?"</u>

7. Can the UKCP explain how the desire to reduce same sex attractions in order to <u>protect one's family</u> is a sign of <u>"oppression"</u> – either external or internal?

8. Does the UKCP affirm that the denial of a client's request to receive help to achieve the type of life goals outlined above is based on <u>scientific evidence that is of such a high standard as to warrant denial of this basic human right</u> in the interest of public safety?

Dermot O'Callaghan has set out these questions in writing several times to the UKCP in the hope that they would acknowledge their reasonableness and address their content, but without result.

Beyond Critique – 3
The Royal College of Psychiatrists
Equal Civil Marriage: a consultation (2012)

Marriage (Same Sex Couples) and Public Health

by Peter May

Summary. *The only medical submission to the Government's consultation on Equal Marriage in 2012 came from the Royal College of Psychiatrists. This has not provided a balanced discussion of the Public Health issues at stake. Their contention that mental health problems in the LGB community can be improved by introducing Equal Marriage as a public health strategy is founded on irrelevant and ambiguous research. Furthermore, they ignore the causes of mental ill health problems that stem from lifestyle factors, which General Practitioners are in a much better position to observe.*

1. The main academic specialties in the Royal College of Psychiatrists are represented by Faculties and Sections. The College also has some Special Interest Groups (SIGs), for example on Spirituality and Philosophy, which provide opportunities for members to meet together, promote discussion and provide support. All members may apply to join them. They are self-selected groups and are not appointed by the College. The submission to the Home Office Consultation came from the "Lesbian, Gay and Bisexual Mental Health SIG" chaired by Prof. Michael King. It was submitted with the approval of the Central Policy Committee of the College.

2. While some SIGs are large and active, this group is not. The College boasts a membership of 15,000 specialists across the world, but a recent survey from the Group attracted just 58 responses, only eight of whom had attended a meeting of the group in the previous four years. Respondents to that survey chose a subject for a symposium, but the event was cancelled through lack of interest. In other words, not many psychiatrists take an interest in this Group. Their report to the Home Office consultation bears only the name of the chairman, Prof. Michael King.

3. The report states prejudicially that to define secular marriage only in heterosexual terms is a form of institutional discrimination on the basis of sexual orientation [1]. Yet children have only ever been conceived through heterosexual union and marriage in all cultures has sought to protect that relationship for the well being of children.

4. The College then gives evidence that public policies can greatly increase perceived discrimination and asserts that the resultant 'minority stress' experienced by LGB people is an important contributor to their health problems.

5. Recently, the mental health problems among homosexuals, well documented in other countries, have been publicly recorded in the UK [2]. In a random sample from the population of 7,403 adults, rates of depression, anxiety, obsessive-compulsive disorder, phobia, self-harm, suicidal thoughts, and alcohol/drug dependence were all significantly higher in homosexual respondents.

6. Is this the result of homophobic discrimination? Perceived discrimination implies having a sense of being discriminated against. It is also referred to as 'minority stress', as it leads to generalised feelings of anxiety, oppression, hopelessness, isolation and sadness. Importantly, in the context of this discussion on public health, that UK study recorded that the level of reported 'perceived' discrimination in UK was comparatively low at 4.9%, being only 3.3% greater than that experienced by heterosexuals in the study.

7. Acknowledging the benefits of UK civil partnerships, the RCPsych submission claims that marriage equality, "will further reduce" the discrimination [3] and lead to greater social inclusion and improved health. The front cover summary sheet states the case more modestly, namely that "marriage equality *could* reduce the discrimination". That anyway is surely possible. But what evidence does the College put forward for their confidence that it *will* reduce discrimination?

8. They refer to the Australasian Drug and Alcohol Review [4] to show that gay and lesbian communities consume more drugs and alcohol than heterosexual groups [5] [6]. For instance, 61% of lesbian women, compared with 24% of heterosexual women, have had a substance disorder at some point in their lives [7]. They then quoted a comprehensive systematic review that shows that the relative risks of gays and lesbians developing substance use disorder was at least twice that of heterosexuals [8].

9. The Review then asks the crucial question of why gay and lesbian people should be more disposed to develop problems with alcohol and other drugs? They concede a number of interrelated factors, mentioning three: meeting places, the difficulties of 'coming out' and discrimination. The Review concludes that "one of the clearest strategies" is to legalise gay marriage *because married people in general have better mental health.*

10. They justify this by saying that health benefits of marriage are not limited to financial advantages. They include access to Government support (which would not actually apply in the UK where it is equally available to Civil Partnerships) and greater social support. No attempt is made to justify the idea that merely calling civil unions "marriages" will lead to improved mental health. In same-sex marriage and heterosexual marriage, we are comparing two very different, self-selected groups. Will both sorts of marriage prove equally health affirming?

11. To support this public health policy, the Drug and Alcohol Review cites the findings Hatzenbuehler et al [9]. This study is also cited in the RCP submission to the Government and therefore needs to be examined carefully. This research was carried out in America, again in a very different context to the UK. In 1996, the US Congress passed the Defence of Marriage Act, defining marriage as a legal union solely between a man and a woman. During the 2004 election, a trend got underway whereby a series of 14 states approved "banning amendments", preventing civil unions or same-sex marriages from being legalised in that state. According to the researchers, this happened in the context of public campaigns fostering a negative climate for the same-sex community. LGB people were confronted with increasing "exposure to stressors, including misleading portrayals and negative stereotypes in the media and hostile interactions with neighbours, colleagues and family members." Unlike the situation in the UK, where discrimination is known to be low, in America overt discrimination was greatly aggravated by these banning amendments, particularly in states which did not have anti-discrimination laws in place.

12. To address the impact of institutional discrimination on mental health, the authors set out to see if there were higher rates of psychiatric disorders among LGB individuals living in states with constitutional amendments banning gay marriage than among LGB individuals living in states without such amendments.

13. The RCPsych presented these findings from America as evidence to the UK Government, that in a nation with Civil Partnerships, where there is strict legislation to control discrimination, and where there are currently documented low discrimination rates [10], that they would nonetheless be evidential grounds to support the introduction of marriage equality.

14. The researchers themselves had drawn rather tentative conclusions from their study. For instance, in states with banning amendments they did find significantly increased levels of general anxiety and

alcohol disorders among the LGB populations. But contrary to expectations, they found statistically significant levels of drug use disorders among those living in states without amendments. They also found statistically significant increases in the prevalence of panic, generalised anxiety and alcohol use disorders among the heterosexual respondents, though the increase was smaller than in LGB populations.

15. They also had other reservations. Only 6 states in the study had some form of protection for same-sex couples. This did not give enough statistical power to test the hypothesis that pro-gay marriage policies would improve the mental health of LGB people in those states. It was possible that in states without non-discriminatory legislation, healthier and wealthier LGB people had moved to states with more liberal policies.

16. They also recognised that sexual identity labels can show fluidity, which could have led to misclassification of some LGB participants over the study period. Neither could they examine whether these symptoms would be short-lived or persistent, once the negative political and media campaigns had subsided. Although this was a relatively large study, the number of respondents meeting diagnostic criteria for psychiatric disorders in states with amendments was relatively small.

17. Therefore, they concluded "the results must be interpreted with caution and they require replication with larger samples of LGB respondents". Yet it was held by the RCPsych submission that these findings provide evidence of the need to introduce same sex marriage in order to reduce mental health disparities in LGB populations in the UK [11]. Unfortunately, this is very weak evidence. It is just one study, in a very different situation from the UK, which shows some conflicting results and calls for more research before any drawing firm conclusions.

18. The RCPsych submission cited a further American study by Buffie, which came to the same conclusion [12]. This is hardly surprising as Buffie, like the Drug and Alcohol Review, depended on Hatzenbuehler's evidence concerning the internalising of discrimination.

19. However, they do not tell us that Buffie makes no distinction in his paper between same sex marriage and civil unions. He uses the terms interchangeably, which adds nothing to the argument in the UK that civil unions should be changed into marriages.

20. Furthermore, Buffie's main argument attributes the poor health record of the American gay community to their lack of access to health care, which would be significantly improved by legal unions. He writes, "Most affected states classify benefits received by domestic partners as taxable earned income." HIV-positive men are twice as likely to depend on public insurance because they lack access to affordable insurance. "Gays in civil unions…had better access to health insurance and quality health care." This undermines the College's position in quoting these American studies. Not only is discrimination low in the UK but we have civil unions and comprehensive health care is free at the point of need. (One would have expected the College to know that!)

21. Buffie goes on to say, "Further time and study are clearly warranted in the ongoing assessment of the more widespread implications associated with embracing marriage equality." He also warns with refreshing honesty that in the study of an emotionally charged issue like this, "we tend to see what is really inside us" and cautions that, despite the peer review process, the results of such studies may ultimately be flawed."

22. The RCPsych submission then asks the pertinent question, *Do LGB people want marriage equality?* They say that "LGB people around the world are interested in having the freedom to marry", and they quote an Australian survey of same-sex attracted people, which found that 78% of respondents reported that they would like to see marriage become available *as an option* for same-sex couples.

23. Yet at least 85% of gays in the UK have declined the option of entering Civil Partnerships, so it is difficult to expect a sudden surge of interest. They may want the "freedom to marry" available as "an option", but most do not evidently want it for themselves.

24. The RCPsych submission dogmatically asserts that opponents of marriage equality produce no evidence to support the claim that the institution of marriage will be harmed by fundamentally redefining it. Rather, they assert that even to claim that equal marriage will harm the upbringing of children contributes to the 'minority stress', which LGB people experience [13]. That may be the case, but it should not stop health professionals from addressing that vital question!

25. It is widely recognised that the 'gold standard' in the upbringing of children is for them to be brought up by their biological mother and father. No-one else will love and care for them as much as they do. Boys and girls need the complementarity of the sexes in their

parenting. Boys need their father and their mother, and so do girls.

26. Now this is a very important matter. The RCPsych claim in their submission that there are no health arguments in favour of denying marriage equality [14]. This is patently not the case. The largest and best study on this subject was published 2012 by the University of Texas [15]. Greeted with vigorous protest from the gay community, the University was forced to withdraw the paper while it performed a thorough analysis of its design, structure, results and conclusions. It eventually gave the study a completely clean bill of health. Any dismissal of its findings now, which is not grounded in a proper discussion of the inevitable limitations of such a study and a sound interpretation of its data, must face the charge of bias.

27. Mark Regnerus surveyed both a large and, importantly, a random sample of American young adults, who were raised in one of eight different types of family arrangement. With nearly 3000 respondents, this was a much larger study than nearly all its peers. Measuring 40 different outcome variables, he compared them according to their family structure. The study clearly reveals that children appear most apt to succeed well as adults if they spend their entire childhood with their married mother and father. The children of women brought up by a mother in a lesbian relationship had the least optimal outcomes (measured in categories such as education, depression, employment status and drug use).

28. Certainly marriages fail and parents die but such things are not planned for. Step-parents usually provide for the best default arrangement. It is quite another thing to set out intentionally to create what we now have good evidence to see as a sub-optimal family arrangement. This puts the desires of the couple ahead of the needs of their children and the well-being of the wider society.

29. Children need the permanent and exclusive commitment of their parents and are unsettled and harmed when that fails. The LBG community, however, has a very poor track record in providing exclusive, stable relationships. As Michael Shernoff wrote: *"One of the biggest differences between male couples and mixed-sex couples is that many, but by no means all, within the gay community have an easier acceptance of sexual nonexclusivity than does heterosexual society in general"* [16].

30. Numerous studies have documented this. McWhirter and Mattison found that all couples whose relationship had lasted more than five years had incorporated some external sexual activity into their

relationship [17]. Exclusive monogamous relationships among gays seem destined to be the experience of only a small minority.

31. Changing the definition of marriage will not bring stability to the world of marriage. As Stanley Kurtz of the Hudson Institute, the American futurology think-tank, has said, *"what gay marriage is to homosexuality, group marriage is to bisexuality."* Bisexuality is more common among women. The aggregate pooling of all recent studies in April 2011 shows that bisexuality is now the largest sexual minority identity label [18].

32. The next logical step therefore from the promotion and full acceptance of homosexuality is the promotion of bisexuality. Kurtz again: *"It is easy to imagine that, in a world where gay marriage was common and fully accepted a serious campaign to legalize polyamorous unions would succeed. We'll someday be endlessly told that not all marriages are monogamous."* [19]

33. As of July 2009, it was estimated that there were more than 500,000 polyamorous relationships in the United States. In Holland and Brazil now three-way polyamorous unions are legal.

34. What other causes of mental health problems besides discrimination might the RCPsychiatrists have mentioned? It is well recognised that there is a higher incidence of general health problems in the gay community, and physical illness itself, as well as bereavement, causes anxiety and depression.

35. Gays and Lesbians are much more likely to suffer from sexually transmitted infections (STIs) than heterosexuals. This is true for all types of STIs. More than a third of all new cases of gonorrhoea are in men who have sex with men [20]. It is estimated that their risks of contracting syphilis, gonorrhoea and HIV/AIDS are some 50 times greater than for heterosexuals. (Although in UK a similar number of heterosexuals suffer from HIV/AIDS, LGB people amount to only 1.5% of the population [21].)

36. Various reasons have been put forward to account for this vastly increased risk. For instance, the tendency of the gay community to engage in risky sexual behaviour is well documented. But the most significant risk concerns the vulnerability of the thin rectal lining compared to the thick musculo-fibrous lining of the vagina. And this risk for disease transmission is present in both giving and receiving anal sex.

37. Despite all efforts, HIV incidence of new cases has remained steady

for 10 years. Latest research shows the HIV rate among men who have sex with men (MSM) in UK is at an all-time high [22]. Analysing data from 1990-2010, it is estimated that without retroviral treatment, which reduces infectivity, the incidence would have increased by a further 68%. Overall, 1 in 20 MSM are infected with HIV, which without treatment takes about 10 years to develop into AIDS.

38. Although 680 people with HIV in UK died in 2011, life expectancy has improved with treatment. In 1996, a 20 year old with HIV could expect to live to 50 yrs. In 2008, that had increased to 66 years. However, the average life expectancy of a 20 year old male is 85 yrs, so even with anti-retroviral treatment, HIV reduces life expectation by around 20 years. This is partly because half of those infected were diagnosed late. It is estimated that one in four people with HIV in UK currently remain undiagnosed, presenting a serious risk of spreading the infection to other partners.

39. The health risks involved in teaching children and adolescents that same sex relationships are equally valid and as desirable as heterosexual relationships, and thereby encouraging teenage experimentation during those years of sexual ambiguity, are unconscionable. Why did the College not mention those vulnerable, adolescent years, when the brain is developing and setting down neuro-physiological pathways through which both responses and memories are formed which can endure for a life time?

40. The estimated annual cost of treatment and care for HIV is £858 million [23]. The savings to be made by preventing new cases, who would now require lifetime treatment, are estimated at £320k per person [24].

41. Several of these infections progress to cause cancers. Cervical, anal, mouth, prostate, liver, lymphoma and skin cancers have all been directly linked to STIs.

42. In general, lesbian, gay and bisexual people have more than twice the rate of suicide attempts of heterosexuals [25]. While women are particularly at risk of alcohol and drug dependence, the men are at higher risk of suicide attempts.

43. Will gay marriage ease the suicide rate? Denmark should provide its LGBT community with one of the lowest levels of discrimination in the world. Same-sex activity was legalized there in 1933, and since 1977, the age of consent has been 15 yrs, irrespective of orientation or gender. It was the first country to legalise same-sex unions in 1989. This provided the basis for a unique study. Over a twelve-year period,

it found that death in Denmark from suicide among men in same-sex registered partnerships was eight times greater than among men in heterosexual marriages [26].

44. Another major cause of low mood is broken relationships. It is recognised that many homosexuals have difficulty forming and maintaining intimate and exclusive relationships. Few things destroy relationships more acrimoniously than jealousy. Then there is the lack of children and wider family ties, which lead to isolation and loneliness, not least in old age.

45. If one is trying to understand the causes of low mood in the lesbian and gay communities, not least in the UK, there are far more powerful forces at work than perceived discrimination and stigma. All these things, in addition to discrimination and stigma, contribute to the poor mental health and high suicide rates found in the same-sex community.

46. Medical science progresses by peer review. Before publication, papers are sent to other scholars in the field for approval. In particular, a Journal Editor wants to know if the authors have been biased and selective in their handling of evidence. No such process appears to have been at work in this RCPsych submission. It seems to be ideologically driven, by authors with undeclared interests, distorting science to achieve political ends.

[1]   RCPsych. College responds to Equal Civil Marriage consultation. June 2012.p.5

[2]   Chakraborty A, King M et al. Mental health of the non-heterosexual population of England . Br J Psychiatry 2011;198:143-8

[3]   RCPsych. College responds to Equal Civil Marriage consultation. June 2012 p.5

[4]   Ritter A et al, Why the alcohol and other drug community should support gay marriage.   APSAD Drug and Alcohol Review Vol 31, pp1-3, January 2012.

[5]   Corliss HL et al. Sexual orientation and drug use in a longitudinal cohort study of U.S. adolescents.   Addict Behav 2010; 35:517-21

[6]   Bolton SL, Sareen J. Sexual orientation and its relation to mental disorders and suicide attempts: findings from a nationally representative sample. Can J Psychiatry 2011; 56:35-43

[7]   ibid

[8]   King M, Semlyen et al. A systematic review of mental disorder, suicide and deliberate self harm in lesbian, gay and bisexual people. BMC Psychiatry 2008;8:1471-224

[9]   Hatzenbuehler ML et al. The impact of institutional discrimination on psychiatric disorders in lesbian, gay and bisexual populations: a prospective study Am J Public Health 2010March;100:452-9

[10]   Chakraborty A, King M et al. Mental health of the non-heterosexual population of England . Br J Psychiatry 2011;198:143-8

[11]   RCPsych. College responds to Equal Civil Marriage consultation. June 2012 p6

[12]   Buffie WC, Public Implications of Same-Sex Marriage. American Journal of Public Health: June 2011, Vol 101, No 6, pp986-990

[13]   RCPsych. College responds to Equal Civil Marriage consultation. June 2012. p5.

[14]   Ibid p.2

[15]   Regnerus M. How different are the adult children of parents who have same-sex relationships?   New Family Structures Study, University of Texas.2012

[16]   Shernoff M. Family Process Journal, Vol.45 No.4, 2006

[17]   McWhirter & Mattison, The Male Couple How Relationships Develop, 1984. pp252-3

[18]   Gates Gary J. How many people are lesbian, gay, bisexual? Williams Institute, April 2011

[19]   Kurtz S. Here come the Brides. The Weekly Standard, 26.12.2005

[20]   Health Protection Agency, 2012

[21]   Office of National Statistics, 2012

[22]   Health Protection Agency Report: HIV in the United Kingdom 2012

[23]   Department of Health. Programme Budget 2009- 2010. Dept of Health 2010 [cited 2012 Nov 2]

[24]   Health Protection Agency 2009

[25]   King M, Semlyen et al. A systematic review of mental disorder, suicide and deliberate self harm in lesbian, gay and bisexual people. BMC Psychiatry 2008;8:1471-224

[26]   Mathy RM et al. The association between relationship markers for sexual orientation and suicide: Denmark1990-2001 Soc. Psychiatry Psychiatr Epidemiol (2011) 46:111-117

Postscript: The Royal College of Psychiatrists and the UK Council for Psychotherapy

Overall, the conclusions of this review document are:

The Royal College of Psychiatrists appears to be the only body in the UK that has taken the trouble to set out a written argument with references to appropriate scientific studies to support the narrative that those who experience same-sex attraction are born that way, that they cannot change and that any attempt to do so is liable to cause great damage to them. It is also the only medical body to make a submission to the Government's consultation on Equal Marriage in 2012. Other professional organisations fall in line on a "me too" basis, so that the general public assume that 'it must be so' since so many independent organisations say that it is so.

Yet the Royal College's arguments are not only unconvincing, but have to twist the evidence in order to make it fit the narrative. This even involves Professor Michael King 'spinning' his own scientific findings and misrepresenting the work of Dr Robert Spitzer.

The UKCP takes the narrative to its next logical stage: therapy seeking to reduce same-sex attractions is automatically deemed to be harmful and therefore must be forbidden. And therapists who support such client requests must be disciplined. The UKCP does not feel the need to establish a scientific underpinning for its position because it considers that other authorities such as the Royal College have already done so. Moreover, the principle of client autonomy, so important in the provision of mental health services, is overridden by stereotyping and stigmatizing any client who voluntarily wants to reduce same-sex attraction as 'suffering from internal or external oppression'.

The result of the positions taken by the professional bodies is that vulnerable individuals seeking to reduce unwanted same-sex attractions are now denied professional help to pursue their legitimate therapeutic goals. A logical consequence of this is that these organisations are making it more likely that amateur therapists and informal church-based ministries will be the only way open to people who want to reduce same-sex attractions, even if they are simply seeking to protect their marriage and family. Such therapeutic approaches will not be supported by professional competencies, protection, regulation, supervision or professional indemnity insurance. This is analogous to promoting the practice of back street abortion, which society has striven so hard to eliminate.

It is time to call the mental health professional bodies to account. They must acknowledge that sexuality is not as fixed as they have suggested. Change is possible, at least for some, change attempts are more likely to lead to wellbeing than to harm, and clients should be free to have their therapy of choice, within a context of informed consent.

Dermot O'Callaghan became aware of the position taken by the UKCP on these matters as a result of action being taken against Dr Mike Davidson, a therapist who was suspended by his professional body for the past year without any charge against him, because of his work in assisting people such as the young man in the example above. There was no client complaint against him; indeed his clients are most grateful for his help to them in working towards achievement of their life goals. He has done nothing wrong, but his livelihood has been affected to the point where he is now trying to sell his house to raise much-needed money.

It is against the UKCP ethical principles critiqued above that such people are judged, but the message of this booklet is that it *is these principles themselves that must be brought into the spotlight.*

Over a period of months during 2012, O'Callaghan corresponded with various representatives of the UKCP with a view to generating a responsible discussion around the ethical guidelines regarding same-sex attraction. Eventually he made a formal complaint against the UKCP, asking that the matter be taken through their own internal complaints procedures.

Their response was that he did not have grounds for a complaint, he merely had a 'difference of opinion' with them. In the first edition of this booklet he commented on the injustice "that if I were a therapist who had the same 'difference of opinion' I could be struck off their register and have my entire career destroyed." Now, three months later, that prediction has come chillingly true. Dr Mike Davidson has been struck off the register of the British Psychodrama Association (affiliated to UKCP), having been investigated under the terms of the UKCP guidelines criticised in this booklet, and told that he "**may re-apply to continue training should you consistently cease to promulgate your current opinions and be clearly able to demonstrate that you would only undertake and advocate work that falls within and complies with the UKCP/BPA Codes of Ethics for Practice ...**"

UKCP letter to O'Callaghan (May 2012)	BPA (UKCP) ruling on Davidson (April 2013)
"... the reason we are not taking your complaint any further is ... because **your different opinion does not constitute grounds for complaint.**" [Emphasis added]	"Your interim suspension has been progressed into full **'removal from the Register' and that you may re-apply to continue training should you consistently cease to promulgate your current opinions ...**" [Emphasis original]
Ms Louise Lilley UK Head of Operations, UKCP	Dr Catharine Kirk, Ms Sheila Foxgold BPA (on basis of UKCP ethical guidelines)

The double standard at work here is palpable. An external critic is not allowed to challenge the UKCP ethical guidelines – even by submitting himself to UKCP's own complaints procedures - because it is said that he merely has a different opinion; yet that same difference of opinion is sufficient to bar a therapist from UKCP accreditation, with consequent loss of dignity and livelihood. This is in effect a *thought crime*.

Dr Arnold Lazarus, Distinguished Professor Emeritus at Rutgers University, warns that, "Organized psychology has been captured by a small group that is dumbing down psychology while pursuing its own agenda .... this oligarchy threatens to destroy the science and profession of psychology, and wreak harm on an unsuspecting public that trusts and depends on psychology."[13]

The UKCP's insistence that it is never in a client's best interests to seek to reduce unwanted same-sex attractions is ideologically driven and devoid of compassion for people who wish to determine their life goals for themselves and their families. The Royal College of Psychiatrists' notion that mental health problems in the LGB community can be improved by introducing Equal Marriage as a public health strategy is without foundation.

This booklet argues for the restoration of good science which will serve everyone – not least those who are lesbian, gay or bisexual. Nobody benefits from bad science.

13   Destructive Trends (back cover)

It is also vital that public discussions concerning same-sex marriage throughout the western world should be informed by the best available scientific research, and not by thinking that is politically correct but scientifically unfounded.